SPIRIT OF
HIGHLAND CATTLE

HEIDI M. SANDS

PiXZ

First published in Great Britain in 2011

British Library Cataloguing-in-Publication Data
A CIP record for this title is available from the British Library

ISBN 978 0 85710 054 2

PiXZ Books
Halsgrove House, Ryelands Business Park,
Bagley Road, Wellington, Somerset TA21 9PZ
Tel: 01823 653777
Fax: 01823 216796
email: sales@halsgrove.com

An imprint of Halstar Ltd, part of the
Halsgrove group of companies
Information on all Halsgrove titles is available at:
www.halsgrove.com

Printed and bound in China by Toppan Leefung Printing Ltd

Introduction

The Highland cow is one of the most recognisable breeds of cattle in the world. Originating in the Highlands of Scotland, with a long shaggy coat capable of withstanding the rigours of a harsh winter, the breed is now exported all over the world. Its reddy-brown colour is unmistakable, but the breed's coat has a wide range of colours, from black through to brindle, yellow and dun. It also has huge characteristic horns that curve and sweep with a graceful appearance in the female, dominating in the bull of the species, giving a strong look, set on a grand head, broad between the eyes; for both sexes carry such headgear.

Once seen as the cow of choice for Highland crofters these cattle are intrinsic to their homeland, for not only are they able to winter out in temperatures as low as minus 20 degrees, they also eke out a life on some of the roughest terrain imaginable with minimal feeding. That's not to say they aren't commercially viable for their beef is some of the finest in the world.

With a shaggy forelock and fluffed up calf at its side the Highland cow endears itself to visitors from all over the world, drawn to its rugged beauty and captivated by its unmistakable look, this truly is the Spirit of Highland Cattle.

Waiting patiently.

Opposite page:
A fine set of horns.

Start them young.

Final preparations.

A fine head.

Opposite page:
Lined up for judging at the Royal Highland Show.

Bellowing to the others.

Opposite page:
Judging underway.

Previous page:
A cow and calf class.

Youngsters of all ages are involved with the showing of Highland cattle.

Preparing to go into the ring.

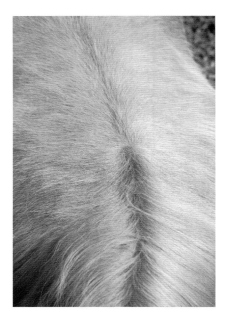

The hair splits down the back to allow
rain water to run off.

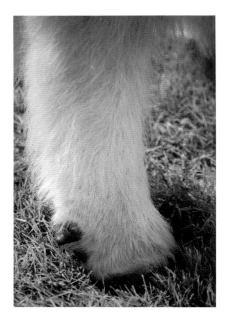

A leg to stand on.

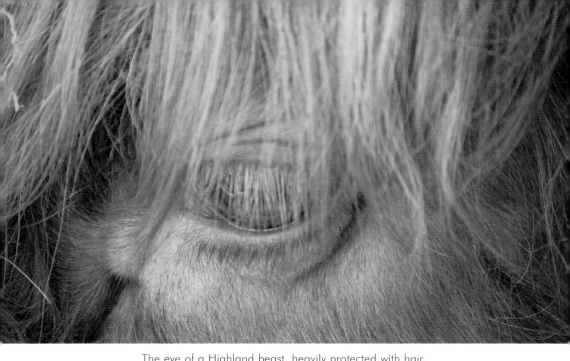

The eye of a Highland beast, heavily protected with hair.

Cow with calf
at foot being
shown together.

In the Grand Parade at Grantown Show.

Ear tags are compulsory.

Combing, the final touch before the show ring entrance.

Opposite page:
Three colours of the breed in line.

A fine set of heads.

Opposite page:
Calves need to walk nicely in the ring.

An adorable face.

Opposite page:
Waiting in the cattle pens at Dingwall mart.

Waiting to be admired in their pen.

Opposite page:
At winter fodder.

At summer grazing.

Opposite page:
In the foothills of the Cairngorms.

Hiding in the bushes.

Opposite page:
The herd.

Perfection in autumn sunshine.

Huge, hairy and Highland.

Part-bred Highland cows
wintering outside.

Right: Standing in
feet of snow.

Highlands in the Highlands.

Previous page: In the lee of the farmstead as the sun goes down.

Opposite page: Shaggy coats protect from the cold.

Getting to those
hard to reach places.

After a shower of rain.

Cattle are usually kept as multiples.

Opposite page:
Off with a purpose in mind.

The Highland cow.

Opposite page:
Cattle usually winter out, being fed hay or silage.

A good mouthful of hay will fill a hungry stomach.

Opposite page:
Feeding from mum.

Easing an itch.

Opposite page:
With winter sun on their coats.

Cattle will eat reeds and rushes.

Opposite page:
A family affair.

As wild as they come.

Opposite page:
This yearling turned to look at the camera.

Lazing on the grass.

Opposite page:
Isn't he cute?

Licking his lips.

Opposite page:
Out at grass.

The whole herd.

Young calves have fluffy coats.

Opposite page:
Calves often form bonds.

Mother and baby.